EROTIX

Literary Journal of Somatics
Volume 1

edited by Zaedryn Meade

Maverick
PRESS

Erotix: Literary Journal of Somatics, Volume 1
Edited by Zaedryn Meade

Find more works by Body Trust at bodytrustcircle.com
Find Maverick Press online at maverick.sugarbutch.net

"every time I fall" by Kat Heatherington was originally published in *The Bones of This Land* from Swimming With Elephants Publications, October 2017. "coming home" by Jen Cross was published in the *Matador Review*, Fall 2017.

The Feast

Introduction

In an erotic embodiment workshop, though we may be loosely organized around a theme of exploration, we all come together with different stories. We have different lived experiences, different relationships to our bodies and to others, different wounds, different resiliency. Many of our stories explore the themes of connection, touch, rejection, care, transformation, power. Some of them overlap at the same resonant frequency, and when we find the tones that match ours, the moment of perfect harmony which comes out of cacophony can be a soothing balm of relief.

I find this to be true in anthologies, too — a group of stories, tied loosely around a theme, manifested through a writer but now a being in their own right — come together with different expressions. Through the various refracted perspectives, sometimes deeper truths emerge. Sometimes a resonance emerges like a singing bowl which can buoy, which can soothe. Sometimes each piece adds it's own perspective on the melody, like the different instruments in an orchestra.

I've had a vision for *Erotix* as a literary journal of somatics, but it's taken me some time to figure out what that is and how to share it with others. That process of articulating something is precisely part, in fact, of what I visualized. When I started to do work in erotic healing circles in the late 1990s, participants and staff alike were often counseled not to talk about it, because others who weren't there and didn't experience this transformative space wouldn't understand. Amy Butcher's essay, "Between Silence and Words," explores this further. But in the two decades since then, we in the embodiment, somatic, transformative, and sacred erotic realms have begun articulating quite a lot — and much of the world is ready to hear what we have to say.

That is *Erotix*'s goal: to be a mouth and tongue to express, in the linear confines of the written word, what it is like to experience embodied erotic transformations. The differences in the content are too many to name — power dynamics, masturbation, temple, sensation from subtle to bold, intellect, skin, orgasm, kink, connection, friction, music, and countless more. Each experience is unique and individual. Yet seeing a dozen or so descriptions come together in one volume shows some commonalities, some themes: the wild and whimsical ways our bodies work, the healing power of pleasure, the navigation of reclamation, shameless exploration, and connecting beyond ourself and other to a greater consciousness all thread through. They also thread through week-long residential workshops where we pray and dance and soar, where we realign our Self and selves, where we circle in a lineage of women's temples.

Though not everyone can be in temple with us, I hope that as you sit with this small volume of words and have a glimpse of what it might be like. Each of these contributors bring their body and desire to the page, and without each one, the circle of this book would not be complete.

sluice

Kat Heatherington

when i ask
to be taken
you give me
back to myself.
what is this light,
this river?
i ask you
to be the current
running through me.
instead, you open
the sluice-gates
and let go
and the river
washes both of us
away.

Engaging in an Erotic World

Alex Jade

Being in your body, to make it feel corporeal, is a capacity developed through self-awareness, sensate exploration, reflection from family and peers, and cultural support. Embodiment is developmental and learned. Through our bodies, we can interface with the world. In our bodies, we can experience pleasure, connection, creativity, and passion. Aligned with other bodies, we can nourish as well as metabolize pain, trauma, and loss. Eros is a through line in our bodies, it is the impulse and the action, a primary life force , and a way we connect with ourselves and with others. Life, breath, creation, death, birth, eros is all of this.

There are many ways in which our erotic capacity is disrupted. Misinformation, aggression, oppression, and trauma lay claim on our bodies. Body Disphoria is a term referring to experiencing aspects of our bodies with unease and incongruence. Dismorphia is a distorted view of some part or quality of our body, and can be expressed in anxiety or obsessive/compulsive behaviors. Physical and emotional trauma can impact how we inhabit our bodies, using strategies of disassociation, numbness, and compartmentalizing to manage our sensate flooding, anguish, grief, frustration, and horror. Finding embodiment practices and erotic energy can led to regain life force.

Skills in erotic embodiment have been more accessible through our own connection and discovery as sex education, access via the Internet, sex positive cultural activities and spaces have emerged. Without a social justice consciousness, this renaissance has led to a divide between bodies. A thoughtful exploration is needed to work within this container of body impact.

Queer erotic pioneers, from experiential data are creating space to explore, celebrate, experiment with our erotic bodies. Through embodied practices and intimate exploration, we have been discovering the sensate and energetic capacity erotic body. Essential in this is identity, embodiment and authority. Joining this is the language emerging to articulate our bodies and experiences.

Play with some ideas to discover more of what your body is capable of. Apply thoughtful awareness to your explorations. Here are some ideas that may be interesting:

> Imagine an erotic experiment that seems interesting, collect the information.

Gather in a group of three or more. Create a form with guidelines and intentions It may be self guided or facilitated.

> Empower yourself to keep as many clothes on as you want, and a resource for identity. If you take your clothes off write your gender pronouns and other identifiers on your skin with a pen.

Access the sensate body through proprioceptors, moving all your joints throughout your entire body.

> Explore your breath, can you feel movement in your ribs, belly, chest?

Lay down and breathe rhythmically, and discover
what happens.

> Explore your body with your hands, can you feel
> energy in different parts of your body.

-Find all the tissues of arousal. Is there a visceral
change as erotic energy swells in the location?
What kind of touch or presence do they enjoy.

> Explore your holes. Do you take in or express
> from this hole?

How do you penetrate?

> How do you receive?

Tell the story of your genitals. Ask someone to
hold you physically and emotional while doing it.

> Write a poem from the language that emerges
> after arousal. Breath into your tissues of arousal
> and listen for the words. It may be one word or
> several.

Working collaboratively, we are uniting our genitals, body erotic
expressions.

There is emerging insight and language coming from the erotic body.
I am curious about what we will all find.

Collage

Megan Jennifer

She steps behind me, close enough to feel her breath on my bare shoulder. "What's your favorite part of your body?" The question drowns in the snap of her knife opening behind my ear. I am equal parts fear and arousal.

"My hands, probably," I shrug.

She walks around to face me. Taking one of my hands in hers, she traces a line in my palm. I watch the tip of her blade slide across my skin, breath caught in my throat.

"Turn around." I do as I'm told. As she slips past me to sit on the black leather sofa, her skirt brushes against my naked thigh. She holds a mug of markers that scare me more than her knife.

A notebook is open beside her. She instructed me to send her two lists: words I use to describe my belly, and words people who like their bellies might use. Compiling the lists triggered waves of shame in me.

"What was the hardest word to send me?" she asks.

"Fat."

"What color would that be?" She makes me choose so I hand her the black one. She writes the word fat on the left side of my stomach.

"What word is most difficult for you to believe about your belly?"

"Beautiful."

"What color is that?" I pick the red marker. The light touch at my side tickles and I jump. *Beautiful.*

"Which word made both lists?"

My face goes blank; I don't remember. "Round," she prompts, before asking, "Why?"

"It's just a neutral, descriptive word," I answer. She uses the purple marker, then adds a few words of her own: *Strong. Resilient. Core.*

We continue until my belly is a collage: *In the way, luscious, big, sexy.* "Is there anything else I need to write on you?" I shake my head.

Taking me by the hand she leads me to the full-length mirror in the next room. "You don't have to feel any certain way. But you have to look."

I avert my gaze.

We hover at the jagged cliff of my reluctance. I make myself peek at the words on my belly.

Ten seconds.

That's all I can bear.

Revealing myself to her, physically and emotionally, is something I choose. Appreciating my own body is an edge I can hardly tolerate.

But edges are for pushing, especially here.

"Will you take pictures please, Ma'am?"

We return to the parlor, as she reaches for her phone and positions me where the light is best. I stand with my hands at my back and watch her grab a red-handled whip with a long black tail. "Pick a word," she commands. I choose *fat* on the lower left side of my belly. She aims the single tail there, strikes a few times. I tunnel into my breathing to process each lick of the whip.

"Pick another word." I can't find the words in my head, can't map them on my body. When I answer *big* she shifts the focus of her whip to the right side of my stomach. I don't flinch.

Shame and desire combust together, ignite around the tinder of pain. I am not entirely in my body while she whips me. As my ability to answer fades, I point where I want her to hit.

She sees me approaching my limit and lands several strokes at the center of my chest to ground me.

"How do you feel about your belly now?"

More than a few seconds pass before I find my voice, "I'm a little bit in awe."

She grabs a marker to write awe. "What else do you feel?"

"Proud." I blush. She prints the word proud over the top of *in the way*.

When she asks if I can take more, I don't hesitate. "Yes, Ma'am." She snaps her whip across my belly a handful of times, then soothes the welts with her hand.

"Good girl, you took that so well." I wear her praise like a medal. She takes more pictures of my belly. "Now you're all marked up, you need photos of that, too."

She tosses her phone and kneels in front of me empty-handed. "Pick a word," she tells me again. I choose *in the way*. She places her hands on my belly, and kisses those words. My eyes close and I slowly shake my head. Tears leak down my face. "Pick a word," she repeats.

"Is ugly on there?" I ask in a quivering voice.

"No."

"Fat," I answer, barely audible. She kisses fat.

My throat is a knot of emotion. She tells me to choose again but I am mute.

"Pick a word." She isn't backing down.

Time freezes between us. I taste the word mercy on my lips, threatening to end the scene. Finally I whisper, "I can't." Tears storm my cheeks. I've never disobeyed her.

"You have to."

Silence. More tears.

"Meg, pick a word."

"Awe," I squeak.

Her lips graze the skin of my belly and I disintegrate. Desperate sobs erupt from my throat. She helps me to the floor beside her, holds me as my tears take over. There is a riot in my head telling me I don't deserve her tenderness. Not by her, not about my belly, not me, not me, not me.

Lulled by the sanctuary of her arms, I open my eyes to her warm smile as she gently teases me for crying all over her. I stand in search of a tissue to blow my nose. She hands me water, pushing hydration after all my tears. "Are you up for some sling time?" she asks.

My clear, direct answer surprises us both. "I want you to fuck me but not in the sling. I need to feel the floor under me." She places a pillow beneath my head as I settle myself on the rug in the parlor. She pulls on a fresh glove, finds the lube, and slides several fingers of her right hand inside me.

My tears start again as she fucks me. She lays her bare hand at the center of my chest, the place I store my grief.

I surrender to her hand inside me; I never want it to stop. I am split open physically the way her kissing my belly tore through my nervous system. I would ride this intensity forever but my body cries mercy. "That's enough," I stammer.

She pulls out of me immediately, removes the sloppy glove. I roll towards her to lay my head in her lap and break into a fresh chorus of sobs.

For the Further Progression of Literary Domination

Karla Linden

"Bind her wrists with
typewriter ribbons

and

tattoo
Anais Nin
quotes on
her thighs."

Blindfolded,
they pull you down
on the bed

newsprint laid out
underneath you

and

the needle
buzzes.

Words form on flesh in between the silence:

Dreams are necessary to life.

then

Each contact with a human being is so rare,
so precious,
one should preserve it.

in Courier typeface,
letter by letter

You wish this dream would never end,
that
the pressure of her hands,
her mouth on yours
and
the hot tattoo needle
raising a welt
with each stroke
would go on 'til dawn.

Between Silence and Words

Amy Butcher

When I first began producing and promoting workshops for an erotic education school, I received this time-honored advice, "Don't tell prospects what we actually do, it won't make any sense to them."

In other words, don't describe in advance the actual activities that happen in a workshop because it will be too titillating—or terrifying—to the uninitiated. Describing the objective activity (e.g., full-body erotic massage) runs the risk of confusing the activity with the source of learning (e.g., how it feels in one's body when giving or receiving a full-body erotic massage). It confuses the *what* with the *why* and that can scare potential clients away.

In fact, this challenge of description applies to any type of risk-taking experiential education. When I led ropes course adventures, we had names for the activities—Trust Fall, High Log, Spider's Web—but everyone understood that it would be the experience of the activity, not the activity itself, which would be the source of learning. An outsider could watch a group try to pass a body cleanly through a big rope "spider's web" but they could only see the magic juju if they could know what was happening on the inside—emotionally, relationally, psychically—of the person being passed. Even when the activities were hard to explain, they weren't problematic in the same way as those in an erotic workshop because nothing on a ropes course was taboo. Wacky, maybe. Challenging, definitely. Out-of-the-ordinary, for sure. But never with the scandalous potential of those in an erotic workshop.

Erotic education workshops are a whole different type of risk-taking activity. In them, a space is consciously created where participants can, through their own bodies and pleasure and with a community of fellow explorers, come into contact with their full potency. Without getting sucked down a rabbit hole of political thought, suffice it to say that some folks can find this potency dangerous and destabilizing. It pushes against cultural norms and assumptions. It connects to powerful planetary forces (this from an atheist). It empowers in provocative ways. After all, the erotic is supposed to be personal, confined to the bedroom, constrained into the context of relationship. To bring it out into community, to detach it from relationship, to use pleasure for personal healing—this breaks rules. As a result, these workshops risk invoking various forms of social sanctioning, and in particular the very personal weapon of shame.

"You did what?!" a friend might ask incredulous as you report on your erotic workshop experience, a mix of curiosity and disgust flitting across their face.

"A G-spot generator. It was kind of a spiritual circle jerk ... really, it was ... " you say, voice trailing off as you realize you may never be able to explain to your friend the potency you felt in that circle. An isolation may grow in you as you swallow the truth of your experience, unable to find words that will make it all make sense, words that will reveal the potency and not call forth prurience.
From the very beginning of our collaboration at Body Trust, we have been trying to find new ways to speak of the erotic workshop experience, to find ordinary words for the non-ordinary experience, to find language that throws off the shame and translates this mystery into a form. It has not been easy.

Twin drawings from Day 1 - PM   *Amy Butcher*

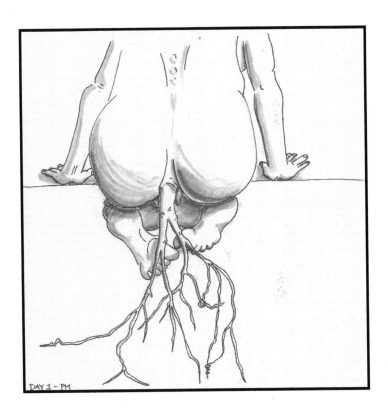

DAY 1 - PM

In one recent experiment towards that end, I served as artist-in-residence at a five-day residential retreat. The intention was to follow the muse, to create art with and for the participants in whatever way it might emerge. My only intention was to stay open, to listen mindfully, and to let whatever wanted to come through me emerge into form.

Image-making might seem like a logical intermediate step between silence and words on the journey towards telling the story of this work, but images are slippery little devils. While words leave a little something to the listener's imagination, images can steal something of the experience and let it loose into the world un-tethered. Some cultures believe that photos and mirrors are dangerous, that they open portals to the Otherworld and thus can allow the soul to leave the body. So, in a workshop where one of the fundamental purposes is to allow the soul to emerge into fullness in the body, images from workshops are problematic at best, bordering on taboo. (Even now, I'm unsure if these images are really mine to share or if they remain private, as much belonging to the participants as to me. If the art was a collaboration, then who gets to share it?)

I began the process thinking my role would be trickster/witness. I planned to sit in the corner during the experiential portions of the workshop, allowing the energy and experiences wash over me and then channel through and out onto the page. I intended to create a visual dialogue within the very community from which the inspiration flowed. I expected to witness and be witnessed, not as performance but as a way of adding a layer impact to the room in the same way that ambient music might. I anticipated being calmly present but slightly removed, certainly not personally on an edge. Wow, was I wrong.

Even as I allowed myself to stew in the energy of the group, sitting in the corner during the experiential portions of the workshop, I could feel my ego get anxious. My ego wanted me to do well, wanted me to draw pretty pictures that would justify my presence. My ego required that each image to be better than the last, like a demanding Kaizan process, so that I would stay relevant. My ego feared that, without the art, I would disappear. Additionally, my ego was tone deaf to the energetic music that surrounded me. It was absolutely the wrong guide for this process of witnessing. I couldn't just send my ego packing, so I had to find a way to befriend it enough to calm it down. So I struck a deal. I set up a structure of creating two drawings during each session: the first would be a kind of magical realism–recognizable but still with vestiges of the non-ordinary; the second, completely energetic with no pretense to representation. The first drawing would relax my ego, letting it anchor itself in drafting skills. The second would flex some new capacities of listening, truly letting the experience channel through me without interpretation or judgment. And it worked. Even though I felt on edge throughout, this twin-drawing practice let me trust the process. It let me get out of my own way.

The resulting twin images "showed" the same experience in two very different ways and, once finished, they were hung in the space creating an expanding documentation of the experience. They also created a visual dialog with the participants, allowing them to reflect on their own witnessed experience and interrogate the art and the artist with curiosity about where it resonated (or didn't) within their own internal experience. Imperfect as they were, these drawings are a starting place to giving the deeper events of workshop a form, to trying to 'name' this non-ordinary experience.

Maybe you 'had to be there' for these drawings to have any resonance. But maybe they will be a bridge if you've never been in a workshop before. Maybe now when you ask, "But what do you do in these workshops?" I can say, "This..." and hand you the drawings. Then, as you reflect on the images, the part of your body that knows its own erotic potency, that is ready to re-member what it feels like to be playing on this non-ordinary playground, will nod — as if tasting a long-lost mother tongue — and say, "Oh yeah, I get it now. Sign me up!"

every time i fall

Kat Heatherington

a small glass heart,
the oakland hills,
a candle burning in bright day.
music i can lean on.
women's voices, arms that catch me
every time i fall.
i am falling the way sunlight
enters a room through a warm closed window
and unfurls along the floor.
i fall and surface and fall again
like a leaf in a whirlpool.
i fall and fall.
your voice on the altar,
one white lily among the gold.
i fall until i am standing,
and it no longer hurts.

How to Have a Body

Porter Witsell

Viviana Iasparra taught me how to have a body. She did this through the ceaseless repetition of precise movements within little choreographies and the cultivation of an analytical relationship with movement and decision. She taught me to trust the intelligence of my physicality and my physical choices, that a well-organized body can then explore all the (non)limits and territories within improvisation, and that improvisation is all the days of a life.

Viviana Iasparra is in her mid 50's. The LEM movement research studio is located inside her house, which is in Buenos Aires. She knocked down the walls of three rooms to make a space large enough for small classes and consequently sleeps on the pull out couch in the living room on the other side of the studio wall. Her son sleeps in the remaining bedroom on the upper floor. Her very large cat, Moo, walks casually through the studio sometimes while we, her students, are breathing heavy, making puddles of ourselves on the grey marbled marley. She teaches movement classes 6 hours daily Monday through Friday and she never looks tired.

There are two phrases that we practiced in every class. One of them, series one, is a movement phrase that keeps the body symmetrical and moves through all levels between standing and lying flat. It can be done once, or it can be done in a continuous loop.

When thinking about learning a piece of movement, one observes the movement and then tries it on. The movements become established and the particularities of each movement can be explored individually or in relation to other details. Examples of this are muscle tone, the placement of the axis, the gaze, momentum, and the coordination of the breath. There is external information as well, information that doesn't come from the body, but is experienced by it. There is the temperature of the room, the sounds, the continued instruction or directives, the texture of the material that you are touching, and maybe other bodies with whom to negotiate space. In any given movement, there is the structural score, the instruction, and the external information. There is also your mood, your energy, your tired muscles, and the option to continue or abandon the project, for example. In any action, there is a constant flow of immense data to process. Viviana says that it takes technique to create a body that is receptive, that can listen to internal and external stimuli and can then make a choice about how to be affected physically. All of these details can be used to move a body; it is choreography and deliberation that elect what images or details to be affected by.

We train in technique to organize the body such that it can make decisions that allow it to act in a space, a space that is always already choreographed by gravity and it's physical conditions. In this way, movement is a place of confrontation and form is a practice of negotiating tensions. Technique is both training alchemy, as well as learning to recognize that some details are simply part of the score. It is using the score to create a physical reality and identifying emotional/physical states (like exhaustion, for example) to be merely one condition of many that affect an action.

Sensation can be the epicenter of movement; it can also be ignored. Viviana stressed the importance of an equal split between the internal and external gaze. Internal gaze refers to any emotional state that might be affecting a movement including a feeling about the experience of moving. An external gaze refers to a focus that is outside of the body, perhaps a fixation on the choreography or task or pure mechanics. The external gaze can be the projection that you see of the movement that you yourself are performing, a sort of internal movie reel.

There was an exercise in which Viviana gave Mailén a specific movement phrase. She was instructed to move continuously through the phrase. After two sequences, Viviana told her to then feel the movement completely, feel it halfway, and then not feel it at all. When Mailén felt the movement completely, there was no communication. My perception was that I was watching a secret. When she felt it halfway, there existed another world that I could access and was being invited into. And when she did not feel it at all, I was in a studio watching Mailén's body do what bodies do, move around. I differentiate these qualities without judgment; each emotional/ physical state can be a deliberate choice. Viviana was partial to the creation of a communicable expressive individuality and believed this was done through practicing the adaptable sensation and the direct decision/action.

Viviana often encouraged us to fall. There are many ways to fall. One can unlock the knees and kind of crumble, or one can explore the tension in a curve to it's full expression until gravity and the center get confused and the result is a fall, for example. There are also many ways to act when one is falling, and/or there are many ways to initiate a fall. The fall can be the goal, or it can be the result, if it is the goal, there can be hesitation, or curiosity, or a brazen flinging, a desire to overcome. You can fake it.

Falls are lessons for navigating risk and commitment. That which overwhelms me I must let go of, or, I decide to be overwhelmed and investigate the directions of that. Viviana made us learn that it becomes necessary to find a certain limit and cross it in order to understand the potential of a movement. If I hope to know it before I physically do it, I will never comprehend the action. Exploring

24

physical limits requires a maximum presence to register how the body manages. Committing with an organized body to an action whose limit I do not understand is the precondition to being able to let go, to let the body fly. A definition of freedom is to awaken the potential to autoregulate one's own process. To act from decision and not habit. Decisions are instances of commitment that give limitations to a context. Viviana said one hundred times that freedom exists within limits.

On Service

Elsha LaRossa

I've engaged with my kinks for as long as I've been sexual, and I've been actively involved in the BDSM community for much of my adult life. It was very early on that I found my identity as a "service submissive." This is not a particularly uncommon identity, yet I've often found myself often involved in conversations with lifelong BDSM practitioners who don't really understand what a service sub actually is. Trying to explain my stance on such a complicated topic at a cocktail party after I've had three Manhattans does not lend itself to the most concise answers, so a while ago I wrote these words to help express myself more fully.

I've always been drawn to submission. The act of yielding control over my choices to a trusted partner is a practice that has always appealed to me on both a sexual and a spiritual level. Anyone who has been to a kink party or fetish night at a club has most likely seen the beautiful tableau of a scantily-clad, masked or gagged submissive on a chain held by a well dressed and slightly imposing gentleperson. But those unbelievably sexy moments are few and far between, and often call for quite a lot of planning and preparation. So, how does one express that submissive identity while not actively engaged in a BDSM scene with one's top? For me, the answer to that question is: service.

So, what is service, to me? The internet tells me that service is "to take pleasure or satisfaction from performing personal services for another." That's part of it, certainly… but only as much as "yellow" is an adequate descriptor for a banana. Sure, it's true… but there's more to it than that.

"Do you like being treated like a servant? You must be into humiliation."

No, not really. Occasional exceptions arise for special individuals. But humiliation is its own kinky game with its own specific rules, and not something I typically associate with service.

Additionally, I take issue with the idea that service is inherently humiliating. Not only do I personally find the practice of serving to be incredibly fulfilling and uplifting, but I think somehow the idea that it would be done so that one can feel humiliated is almost, well, hypocritical. If I were serving to be humiliated, all focus in the moment would be on me, not the task at hand. In that case, the only person I'd be serving is myself, which means I wouldn't be serving anyone else very well at all… which sort of defeats the purpose, don't you think?

"So is this a sex thing for you?"

In service to someone with whom I have a strong connection, the primary emotions I feel are generally warmth, respect, and deep trust. Often there's a little dose of adoration thrown in as well. While they are powerful, good feelings, none of those emotions (in my mind) are inherently sex-oriented. Service, for me, does not need to be a sex thing. But then again, on the other hand, a lot of times I really enjoy having sex with people for whom I feel a warm respect, deep trust, and a hint of adoration. Don't you?

That said, I absolutely feel that my service-oriented identity

27

influences my sexuality. When I'm intimate with a partner, the thing that pleases me the most is their pleasure. I'm chameleonic to an incredibly high degree, depending on the feedback I receive from my partner. I can find equal levels of gratification from tender, soft caresses and brutal power exchanges with hair-pulling and face slapping. All I need is to see that whatever we are doing is what you need. I am here to serve you, to be what you want me to be... and that's the sexiest thing I can think of.

"How much can you possibly get out of this?"

When it clicks like it should? You have no idea how much.

I give: My time, attention, and focus to the interests of my top, as though they were my own. I offer my support when it's needed or wanted. I want them to know they don't have to accomplish huge efforts without help.

I get: Reassurance that I can do things that matter. Confidence in myself when I've done things well. The enjoyment of service for its own sake– being able to help someone when they need it is a massively rewarding feeling. Yes, recognition by the top is nice, too. A warm, happy, "Thank you" can make my day, or sometimes my week. I don't really need anything flashy or showy for recognition, just a quiet smile, a hug, a kiss. In the words of someone dear to me, "Service isn't about 'look at me!' Service is about 'oh look, it's done!'"

I also get the opportunity to express devotion and other complex emotions in a way that feels safer, steadier, and often quieter than the emotional free-fall that, say, a traditional romance or deep relationship normally entails. Emotions are scary. Energy is overwhelming. Sudden fits of passion are unpredictable. In service I can feel all of these things within a context... I know where to step. I know what to do. I know how you'll react. And then, when it's over, the things we've built are, on some level, *our* things — which is tangible evidence of our relationship that I can look to in moments of uncertainty or doubt or absence.

So, no, I don't dream at night about bussing your tables. I don't long to take your coat. I don't care about mixing your drink. I sometimes do these things, and even more things I would really rather not do... because it was asked of me by someone who is very important to me, which is enough to make them matter. That's why they call it 'submission' and not 'waitressing.'

Serving, and knowing I am representing my top well, that I'm following through with grace, that they have confidence that I will do the best job I can (and that the best I can is good enough), warms me more than enough to take most tasks in stride, or even cheerfully. And that makes me feel indescribably happy, beautiful, and fulfilled.

From Wanting to Being

Cooper Taite

The twentieth-century French existentialist philosopher Maurice Merleau-Ponty argued that everything about being human is contingent, but it is through the interactions of the body that a form of existence is constantly being created. Who and what we are as humans is constantly being negotiated through the situations that we, as our bodies, encounter in the world. It is the body that is able to take the contingent and conditional and make it a reality. However, for some, the body cannot produce the change necessary to successfully navigate the change in situation. In these cases, people look for equipment in order to facilitate the needed change. For some who enjoy restraint and bondage play, the equipment used helps them successfully navigate the sexual terrain to become sexual beings.

To quickly illustrate the concepts of possibility and bodily change, Merleau-Ponty uses the example of someone who wishes to fall asleep.

"As the faithful, in the Dionysian mysteries, invoke the god by miming scenes from his life, I call up the visitation of sleep by imitating the breathing and posture of the sleeper. The god is actually there when the faithful can no longer distinguish themselves from the part they are playing, when their body and their consciousness cease to bring in, as an obstacle, their particular opacity, and when they are totally fused in the myth. There is a moment when sleep 'comes', setting on this imitation of itself which I have been offering to it, and I succeed in becoming what I was trying to be… The body's role is to ensure this metamorphosis. It transforms ideas into things, and my mimicry of sleep into real sleep."

In this manner the possible idea of "I could be a sleeper" is gradually changed into the reality of being a sleeper as the body is able to make the necessary navigations in the situation by acting on the idea and turning it into a reality.

Looking, now, to the concept of intimacy, we see that a similar change has to take place. We often say that this change is getting "turned on" or being "in the mood." It is a change that is located both in the physical and psychical area of the individual. If Merleau-Ponty is right, and I believe he is closer than most, then it is the body that must go through the motions and begin to navigate the change. For some this comes rather easily. Those individuals may go through the change of wanting to be a sexual being to actually becoming a sexual being very easily. Others need time in order to navigate the change. This time of change is designated as foreplay.

If an outside observer was to watch a couple during foreplay and a couple during intercourse, for example, the similarities of actions between the acts would outweigh the differences. Foreplay is simply the mimicry of the sexual act. It provides the body with the guidelines and the roadmap to navigate its change. The consciousness within the body changes from that of potentially wanting to be sexual to knowing no other way of being.

The sexual state can be accurately, if not simplistically, described as one of desire. The body desires to be sexually stimulated, but it also desires to be desired. In an initial sexual relationship, the sexual being is free to both desire and be desired. This has to do with the nature of the body and its situation. As a subject in the world, I choose and then act on those choices. I have a personal consciousness that sets me apart, in my own perspective, from everything else. This is mirrored in being the one who desires. But my physical body is an object in a world of other objects. It is there to be acted upon by the wills and acts of others. This relates to the object being desired.

For some individuals, the ability to make the change into a sexual being is a fraught activity. There could be a variety of reasons why someone may try to hold back from the world of desire and sexual satisfaction. If they try to hold their consciousness back from being "turned on" the body can never engage in the mimicry of sexual activity that it needs in order to make the change. For those who, for a variety of reasons, need or want extra help in changing into sexual beings, BDSM practices can help facilitate this.

Foreplay in many BDSM relationships begins with rituals. These rituals can be behavioral, physical, and mental. This essay will only look at the physical. For those that integrate bondage, the restraints and the restraining of the submissive takes a central place in the foreplay act. By limiting the body's potential to act in the case of the submissive, the restraints help the individual navigate into the position of object to be desired. For the dominant in the relationship, the placement of restraints on another is the visual foreplay needed in order to navigate to the more subjective side of sexuality — the being who desires. The submissive may now be "turned on" because the body is mimicking the expected sexual being — the desired object. The restraints help to simplify the situation that the individual needs to travel in order to become sexual.

To help simplify the transformation even more, a bondage hood or other type of sensory deprivation device can be used. Some people, and I count myself as one of them, need to be in positions of control. However, that does not mean that they could not take the submissive's position. What it could mean is that they need more help in navigating the change from their natural dominant mode to a mode as sexual object. Thinking of a simply restraint, the limbs and perhaps the torso are immobilized, but the basic center of interaction with the world, the face, is open. With the face open to the world, the body is still able to interact with the world. If this is an option, then the individual's body will try to respond and exert its own will on the world. The reactionary posture that comes from the senses can be enough to frustrate the sexual navigation because the body is trying to navigate to a position of power that is, while restrained, impossible for it. To help aid the navigation, then, the submissive can be blindfolded, gagged, or given other apparatuses, such as the bondage hood, to cut their senses off from the world. With their main mode of input from the world cut off, the body is forced to assume the position of submissive. Without input, the subjective side of the body is cut off allowing the objective nature of the body to emerge. It really has no other choice. Once the body realizes its situation, it can be led by the restraints to assume the position it needs to be in to become the sexual being — one that is to be desired.

In these ways restraints act as a technology or a key that allow the body to make the necessary changes into a sexual being. Perhaps a bit paradoxical, the technology liberates the body by depriving the body of its normal mode of interaction with the world. By taking away the body's ability to interact with the word in its familiar and habitual manner, the restraints and hood of bondage allow the body to assume the position of a sexual being, and in assuming that position, the body can adopt the mode of a sexual being.

silence shapes the rhythm

Kat heatherington

rain, drumming on the earth
drumming, pausing, and drumming through our hands
pat tap slap caress and sigh of falling water
through arching bodies and into the earth outside—
        you have the wisdom to do this—
water from the sky, water in the pools, water
dancing in a tear-filled gaze.
on the last day, a rainbow.
in the morning i rise and dance and dance,
standing still breathing,
watching your eyes i dance,
heart to heart without moving we dance,
and your eyes dance,
watching rain and hands and bodies
learning this wisdom
opening to water, ebb and flow
in the sacred trust of our bodies
wise upon the earth.

and then in night silence
the sigh and scent of hot water steaming
beneath an infinite spill of stars.
surge and pause and surge again—and pause—
our bodies know this pulse.

roll of thunder down red cliffs,
driving storm of the mountain west.
cottonwoods shake their leaves on the riverbank,
roots twining through mud and rock,
glint of sun on the wing of a dragonfly.

in the night, hands and tongues open gateways,
further mysteries, body and breath,
and the gate stands open in the morning light,
self-knowledge awakening.
hunger rises in the heart, desire without object,
awareness of a space that wants filling.
i carry that space alongside the fullness
of Circle, and surrender.

trust in a process i only partly understand,
yet see in my body, embodied—
if i am closed, i will open
if i am empty, i will be filled again.
if i am full, i will overflow,
and turn toward emptiness.
surge and pause and surge again—and pause—
the silence shapes the rhythm.

days later, rain on the roof as my hands
ride the body of my lover, rain
in a dry place, a dry year, falling and falling.
as the night wears on, the miracle,
not stopping.
dawn breaks red and gold on a land gone dark with water,
absorbent, reflective, shining.
water stands in sunlit fields,
green with life, golden with light,

radiant in this trust.

winged expansion furls into necessary containment
a bowl at the base of my spine.
in that bowl, a blossom
opening and closing in the heartbeat of days, weeks,
drinking and creating
the sweet clear nectar of the root.

The Opposite of Vicarious

Val Prozorova

Orgasm came rarely to his body.

Lovers had tried, with fingers and lips, with rough thrusting and awkwardly whispered words, but beyond a general throbbing after, and a few muscles tugging the next morning, he felt little to nothing at all.

He supposed he was one of those idle statistics that suggested his body just couldn't experience that pleasure. No endorphin rush, no trembling limbs, no hot-cold flushes and hitched breath. Things he wrote of so often for his own pleasure, and read about, but things he himself could never experience.

I didn't matter in the end, he figured. He was a statistic in everything else.

He'd read somewhere that while men watched their porn, women read theirs. For some reason, that had always lingered with him, tugged at something deep in his belly. Perhaps that was why he wrote stories that had others biting their lips and squirming in their seats; emailing him anonymously to admit that they had had the orgasm of their life, touching themselves while reading about the men he brought to life on the page have the orgasm of theirs.

Vicarious living.

Vicarious screwing.

Vicarious orgasms on the page and off it.

The first time he had experienced genuine sexual pleasure as a woman was at the words of an abusive partner. His mind had been filled with smoke and mirrors, demands and decisions made for him, promises of being shown off as a boy, dressed as a boy, taken as a boy, spanked as a boy, while his own fingers drew wetness between his own trembling legs, face pressed smeared to the phone that trickled poison into his ear.

He'd left the relationship battered, never once having felt the palm of his lover at all, and wearing all the scars of the words they'd used instead.

After that, birthdays came and went, and sex stayed stale. Over and over were repeated words like *such a good girl* that made his skin crawl rather than tremble. Over and over were fingers pushed deep where he would rather have them wrapped around an organ he didn't physically have. Over and over indifferent lovers, smeared semen, salty aftertaste, dewy drops of lube lingering in wiry hair.

It could have been worse. He could have been having no sex and contact whatsoever.

It could have been worse. He could have been in a relationship where sex was abusive, not a pleasure, again.

It could have been worse, and it wasn't, so what right did he have to complain?

His first true orgasm came at the hands of an unexpected lover, who whispered, wet words and hot breath against his cheek, that *my boy's looking toned this week.*

His boy.

Touching a form that didn't fit the term, breasts large and unwanted, thighs hiding between them private heat beneath a thatch of dark hair. And yet, even there, with his lover's face pressed to his chest, with his fingers seeking to press there between his legs, and pressing, to him he was *his boy*. To this lover, he was real, for the first time in his life.

He'd never felt more vulnerable, nor more powerful, than when he watched his partner sit back and suck his fingers clean, delighted by the outcome. He'd never before experienced that shiver, that utter breathless anticipation, than when his partner leaned close and folded his fingers over his eyes.

Just like that, he'd said. *Just stay that way for me, good boy.*

He stayed.

He obeyed.

Good boy.

His breathing hitched and his thighs trembled as they were spread and his underwear pushed aside for a hot tongue to seek within. Behind closed eyelids, he wasn't in a body that didn't belong. Behind closed eyelids he was himself, legs spread and hand down tugging his lover's hair, voice pitching higher and higher with every deliberate and practiced lick.

This wasn't a manipulation.

This wasn't a gross promise undelivered.

This was one man pleasuring another, seeing past the physical body to the one beneath, enjoying filling his mouth with the essence and heat and wetness of him.

Moaning for it.

He'd never come so hard in his entire life.

He'd never come so many times in a row in his entire life.

Behind closed eyes, he was the characters he wrote himself into over endless pages, he was the men people read about and talked of, he was the lover wanted by another, not found wanting. He was himself, and his lover loved him for it.

He hardly heard the words of pleasure and praise as his partner kissed his way up his trembling body. He hardly heard anything for the rushing in his ears and the thudding of his heart. He laughed when he was reminded that he could open his eyes again, that his lover was there, that he wasn't going anywhere.

Behind closed eyes, he was who he always knew himself to be. And opening them then, and seeing the grin, crooked and smug, of the man who had undone him, hearing the playful comment about how *that's just a thing I do, sometimes*, feeling the other's genuine desire for him… in that moment he knew that he was himself here, too.

Transcending words and paragraphs of vicarious living, vicarious screwing, vicarious orgasms, to finding pleasure of his own.

Then you'd better do that again, was all he managed, setting a hand to the other's skinny shoulder to guide him back down once more.

coming home

Jen Cross

excerpt

November

Change   the   world   by   telling   it   differently   this
time   say   it   backwards,   start   with   the
good part   the messy part   start   with   the
aftermath   how he got his clothes back on   how   his
shirt was buttoned up wrong   start with the description
of his christmas lights all gone askew   how his hamster
 squeaked in its wheel all the way through it   how his mom
knocked on the floor, on the stairs at the bottom of the landing
 to ask if you wanted cookies   tell it differently
tell it differently   this time, say how you screamed.

December

In my dream I have three orgasms, two in the shower with water and
the last in my room, like in a dorm, my room is messy, clothes are
scattered but I have a small vibrator and I use that one in my room,
but it's slow, the battery is wearing down, and then my stepfather
comes in, he wants to go do something but I ask him to leave so I
can finish, indicate the vibrator, make it clear what I'm doing, and
he leaves, I think *I should have asked him to help* but it's not what I

want and he doesn't throw a fit and then my friend D is right outside, too, looking at the art on the door of the room next door. So the vibrator isn't loud because the battery is wearing out and it's hard to get enough pressure or stimulation but then it's enough and it's almost like my labia are stretched out very thin and tight, tense, and I do have another orgasm while I'm laid out on my bed with my head at the foot, on top of the covers. I'm not hiding under the blankets. There are lots of boxes against one wall. Then we're leaving, going somewhere, and I was supposed to have a workshop that day but no one signed up but someone *could* drop in so I go in, to put a sign on the door saying the workshop is cancelled. I go in twice. The first time I forget, I'm distracted, and the second time I think I wake up before I can see whether I'm distracted or not. I forget what distracts me. It's a last minute thing, this plan to leave, to go out, to go somewhere with him—in the dream, it wasn't on my agenda for the day, but I have some compassion about it now

January

Last night I masturbated even though I knew it wouldn't do any good   wouldn't stop this or release me from the heat and weight and pound of need that I could say was just my crush but really, more, is this surge of freedom, stories shoved down, that suddenly understand that they have a way out. Anyway, last night I was masturbating and I couldn't focus   I was imagining this crush, her face, how she would look if we (I had to not write *when we*) finally kissed, how she sounds when she says my name, and then I was off and running and then stuck too in dry and sensation because I never masturbate imagining *myself* in the scene   I always use strangers   watching   outsiderness and then put myself into the body of one of the guys (just to feel something   friction   power   just to come). But last night I was alive and everywhere, I was fucking all my

43

friends, god, finally, the consummation of all that longing and energy, I was making out with him and playing with them and going to SM classes and sex parties and getting fucked in the middle of a crowd. I was afraid to imagine all these things and then I was flying through them, spinning, couldn't stay in any one place for very long because I want all of it, I want friends and laughter in my bed, yes, maybe even you, too, if you can be present with this all of me (and if I can be present with the all of you).

Here's what I thought this morning: *This is the opening after so much closure. Of course, it would look like this. Of course it would be this big. Years of shoving down strata of longing and when dam breaks, girl, it doesn't open gradually.*

May

Today's was a fantasy that shifted like a dream, from me on my knees before you to you on your knees before me, from us in the classroom to us in the wings of a theater, from you about to come to me, yes, coming, there under the water—I fell in, let images unfold, told myself the story the way I'd write it, the way I'd tell you if we were on the phone. I made myself wait for the good part, made myself listen for zippers and instructions, smelled chalk dust and sweat. I got too excited, had to pause, panting, eyes closed, *oh god I'm so close.*

What nudged me just that last inch over the edge was the image of my own cunt, exposed to you just when you can't react, when no one else could see but you—and in my own mind's eye, that omniscient narrator of fantasies, I could see, too. I came hard, voyeur and exhibitionist, imagining you taking what had been so brazenly offered to you. Of course, in your taking me, in my own fantasy, I take myself. I am getting off to the image of my own body, your impotent arousal, my own swollen audacity.

February

1.

Just because you've had enough
doesn't mean you wanted too much
—Dean Young, "No Forgiveness Ode"

Just because you set your foot down on one great truth too many
just because you are tired of not being able to breathe the right
way   just because you know you used to be able to engage in
unbarren conversation   just because the heartache lives in your
arms   in unsaid words   in the palms of your hands just   because
you are done with denying you turn on the light one day and look
at the poem taped to the wall   *wherever you are, no matter how*
lonely, the world offers itself to your imagination   and you feel
imagination rise up in you like a hunger   an unfed thing   n o t
broken   not gone lost or disappeared you feel it shifting under the
garbage and other   people's promises under the blankets that
you draped over it, telling it *someday*   its   movement   stings
and stretches at your belly   tears something holy in you open
         names an old vice clings sudden and damp to the inside of
your mouth and you come to understand that you have found your
someday you have met   in your own ordinary bathroom   t h e
day you are going to stretch your new wet wings open and away into
your own life.

This is a plain thing   almost unmentionable   but   it
happens every day   you understand   there in
your shower-slick hair and wrapped in yesterday's towel   that
your life has split you open and let you into it.

There is no clanging of bells   no one pats you on the back
the person who you will hurt the most with this new flight does not

45

say *thank you*   does not say *congratulations*   you get no
certificate   no plaque   no medal   you   get
only the rising song of your own unseparated heartbeat
 every day a new physicality in your chestyour wristsyour neckyour
bellyyour anklesyour gut   this is how it is just because you let your
imagination breathe and listened to it whisper *now* into your inside
ears   this is the thing   you leaned your own whole
self into that *now* and then you answered it: *Ok*   you listened
and said, *Ok. Now.*   this is the incidence of implosion t h e
wreckage of all those overly-constructed catacombs   the maze you
made to contain all your living and unliving parts   the day you
said ok and meant it   that was the day all those parts snugged
their hands together   tangled finger into finger   remet   one
another that was the moment everything broke and was new
the tears for this moment aren't shapely   a r e n' t t e l e v i s e d
      are only yours   in one quiet, steamy bathroom   with
dirty clothes on the floor   your hair uncombed   drips of
yesterday's dirt still smearing their coagulations on the mirror
 you feel it small and real in you like a just-conceived thing   you
put hands on your belly   one atop the other   you   smile,
even though everything is breaking.

2.

Keep breathing. Inhale it all. She writes me then is gone. This part is
new, not being the furtive one. I want all this newness, the way I have
to learn new ways to be in my body because the old ways don't fit in
my hands anymore. And that makes this moment very different. I
skin my knees, breathe hard, I am ready for this orange flood. I say
thank you thank you thank you.

46

My Beauty, Being Seen

Misha Bonaventura

We had the place to ourselves.

He started setting the scene.

He sat me on the only piece of furniture that was not dungeon equipment, a plain wooden bench.

He prepared his tools on the floor; spread out his ropes, lined-up his whips. I sat in anticipation. He spread my legs and kneeled before me. He had me touch myself; spread my pussy lips so he could see my pussy. He said nothing. I was hot and uncomfortable under his gaze.

The theme of the weekend was being seen in my beauty.

The intensity of this thing I so desire — to be seen — was overwhelming.

I took a deep breath.

He chose his tools and started whipping my thighs as I continued to touch myself. The softness of my lips curling around my fingertips was intoxicating. Slow and soft, the dragon tail whips were supple at this velocity. They kissed my thighs, which were both excited and scared. He walked away and picked up a single tail and cracked it on the floor. My whole body tensed at the sound. He was gathering the energy, and as the tips touched my skin they were like electric shocks to my system. When he switched to the single tails they were like bee stings. I moaned, I was scared, I hurt, I loved it. I wanted to be good; I wanted him to want me. I came under my own fingers and his skillful presence.

I was high with pleasure and looking into my eyes he wrapped the dragon tail around my neck and I was gone before I even knew what he was doing.

In the 4 seconds I was out I was lucidly dreaming. It felt like the future. He held my head and smiled at me, "You're okay. There's no one safer to do that with."

In an ultimate act of surrender my breath was taken away and I died. Coming to I was soft but also furiously madly in love. He was both my killer and my savior. He took me, and I liked it.

I love being violated.

How do I resolve this desire to be both deeply honored and deeply violated?

I trust him right now. That's all that counts. He's getting in deeper.

He let me come back slowly.

Everything was in slow motion. He busied himself with arranging his tools. He hypnotically gathered his ropes skillfully zigzagging them between his thumbs to create a neat bundle. It was mesmerizing. All I could do was watch. Hypnotized.

All of my training tells me this was totally fucked up. My whole body tells me I am completely turned on. While I should probably not have felt safe with him, I did. I love breath play, I love living on the edge, I love dying. I love the ultimate surrender to another. I love feeling cared for by this loving Dom.

I should be furious. I should slap his face and tell him he should never have played with me in that way without negotiating it ahead of time. I should... I should...

The shoulds just fade into the back of my head in the most amazing natural high I've felt in a long time.

As I arrive back on this planet he asks if I'd like to feel some rope.

I say I'm ready.

He goes to the bathroom and I begin to dance. The music takes over my body and I feel how delicious it is to move. I imagine this moment as a rebirth of my spirit, the movement of my body, the freedom to be fully self-expressed. I love to dance. I'm alone in my body with the music as my muse and feeling my body being so alive.

He returns and arranges his ropes. He tells me to keep dancing. He'll work around me. We dance the ropes on together. We push and pull. We spin. We kiss. It's effortless flow. My high goes even higher and all of a sudden I'm on the floor in full body orgasmic bliss, tits and torso bound making love to him and to the world. He slaps my pussy again and again and I'm sent beyond the stars. The orgasmic energy rushes through my palms and my feet and we are inside each other creating the ultimate art. It makes no difference that his cock is not inside me, we are acting as one, he has penetrated me and I have received him.

My ultimate gift of "yes" is his alone. I surrender.

Somewhere in the background people have come into the room and they are swooning over our scene. I can hear them fawning over his talents and talking about dancing. The woman approaches me; she asks if we can dance. Unable to make any decisions, I look

to his guidance. He says he needs to take a break and gives me over to her. We dance and I kiss her momentarily and then one of her companions comes to tell me how incredible it was to watch our dance. He tells me I'm beautiful and that my beauty was enhanced by being met with a master. The compliment was true and I allowed it to penetrate me, breathing it in.

I deserve this level of skill. This is the only kind of sex I want.

And then he was back. My loving Dom wrapped me in his gaze and we shared the beauty we had created together. What a blessing to be witnessed in our glory. We deserve all of this attention. We reflected our talent, our beauty, our flow to each other and we fell in love in that moment. Eyes locked, breathing together, beauty in the creation, ultimate art making.

Meanwhile, our audience had gotten in a quibble with each other. The energy was too much for them to handle and they had to bring themselves down. I asked him if we could ask them to leave. He said no. Instead he grabbed me by the ropes around my breasts and dragged me to the back porch. I love how he handled this, it was so subtle but so skillful. In this moment he embodied the creativity of all needs met by me, by him, by them without disturbing any of us. He fucking handled it. I was so turned on.

Outside he had me in a trust hold, leaning me back to the brink of falling. I had flashes of my head splitting open, my arm breaking, my desire to be safe overwhelmed my system. He penetrated me with his gaze and said, "Thank you for trusting me." I replied, "Thank you for holding me." I burst into tears, and then screamed, and then roared. I let all my frustration out for all the men who dropped me. I screamed for all the men who ever said I could surrender into their arms and then failed to follow through. I roared for my own knowing that I am the only constant and I am solid. I screamed for my deepest desire to surrender into the loving arms of my partner.

Then he took me to the sofa and let me hold him. He suckled on my tit and allowed me to fill him back up with love and nurturing. Tenderness. We spoke the words we were feeling in the moment and breathed together. He said he felt vulnerable. It felt like the rebalancing of the energy between us. He asked me to sleep with him...no expectations, just be together for the night. Of course I said yes.

We headed back to the room but got diverted to the hot tub. Our friends from earlier were there and they proceeded to lovingly objectify my tits and soon the entire hot tub was giving me attention. I could feel their eyes on my breasts. I breathed through the attention. I can handle this. I can stay present. I will let you reflect my beauty. Breathe.

Then my loving Dom started dancing me again. He began to pull me around the tub and manipulate my body. I surrendered to his touch and trusted his care and attention. The voices of the people were drowned out by the rush of water past my ears. I arched my back and opened my eyes and dove into the star speckled sky. I embraced the universe and died again in his arms.

He asked me for one word to describe this moment.

My word was Cosmic. His word was Integrity.

Blood Let

Jennye Patterson

A scar can be a beautiful gift, a permanent mark that releases negative energy and permanently changes someone's relationship to their body for the better. It can also be a source of continual aggravation, embarrassment, and resentment. And it binds the two of you together, as long as it lives, because there is no way that somebody can look at a scar without thinking of the person who made it... Once made, a cut cannot be undone. Slice wisely, or not at all.

— Pat Califia

I get deep down into the place where it's rooted in my skin and pluck away at it, playing it like a musical instrument—the fingers pressing, making the pain worse before it can get better. Then out it comes. No more discomfort, no more ambivalence. Until another needle pierces the skin. That's what writing is for me, an endless cycle of making it worse, making it better, but always making meaning out of the experience, whatever it may be.

— Gloria Anzaldúa

*Jacques Derrida writes about this desire we all have
to mark loss, to record memory physically. Derrida
argues that it is not that we desire to mark the
moment of trauma, of the wound, but rather that
we often need to and want to record the moment
just before it... Marks made as talismans against
loss.*

— Chris Abani

A ritual:
You carve a triangle onto my chest— I squeeze and press my skin,
drip blood onto the fabric spread out in your open hands. Stitch
round and round and round (me).

+++

A ritual:
21 G1 1/2/ hip in hip/ lie back lean forward/ push gently then firm.
More, harder, re-line lines.
Make an x.
Push in, harder

Now you.
It's so fresh, purest red bubbles up, I want to lick it.
Long thin lines, tracing, tracing,
reach in and pull out.
What's trapped in there?
You ask: can it loosen? Can it be left behind?
Deepest breath like ones that puff my chest out,
your eyes on my eyes.

Hold your hand over it,
take a picture.
The mirror mirrors;

it's an opening.

It stays.

+++

The fact of his pulse
the way he pulled his body in, out of shyness or shame or a desire
      not to disturb the air around him.
Everyone could see the way his muscles worked
            the way we look like animals,
                  this skin barely keeping him inside.
      I wanted to take him home
and rough him up and get my hands inside him, drive my body into his
      like a crash test car.

— Richard Siken

+++

Sometimes I want to dig my nail into your wrist, move from being marked to doing the marking.

+++

"How do you caption smoke?" She said: "You'd have to trap it first."[1]

Fingers on telephone keys, trying to find letters to make words to find you.

I am a tiny embroidered circle. I am using my hands and then yours to ride round and round myself. Make homes around myself. Make homes in myself.

---

1   Bhanu Kapil, Ban en Banlieue

Sometimes the work is avoiding the work, Liz[2] says. Or: sometimes it is diving clear into it, no life boat or vest of a friend nearby to pull me back out.

Sometimes I don't want to come out.

Sometimes black holes are safest, no one can see me searching for homes in your skin. No one but me can hold my long-haired tendrils, waiting to be ripped out. Let go.

Sometimes letting go is the letting in. Sometimes letting in is the letting go.

Sometimes the actual. Sometimes the invert.

Sometimes I am riding on an ocean crest, your hand in my cunt and there is a demon-faced sheep or something watching us and sometimes I find that comforting.

Your hand in my cunt I find comforting.

I want all of your hands in my cunt, I want new hands in there, I want you to open me up so wide I never go back to being shut.

+++

How I desperately want someone to touch me in the center of the intensity, how ravenous the wanting makes me, how starved, how unmet the hunger is. Knowing we can never actually touch, not there.

I feel alone in a deep solitary way and maybe there was never anything except this feeling. Bandaids on top of old on top of new

2   Liz Latty, writing date on 5/29/12

wounds and never healing. Skin becoming no longer just skin but now wearing the extra girth of scars. Running my finger over them. Tearing them open. Drinking what comes out, refueling.

Find me.

+++

A ritual:
Felt a ghost of violence-past pass through me while you were kissing me,

 pressing into me.
Writing from inside the trigger.

I needed to pull away, didn't want to hold the shape of the ghost, that feel, didn't want to hold that ghost while I held you, too, but I couldn't get that ghost to leave.

How fucked up that choosing felt:

Ride inside the ghost body that wants to bring me back to a night when someone stuck their cock in me while I cried— stopped and then began again.

or

Push past that presence and into your mouth again. Trust that maybe I could glide past it and not get frozen in place forever.

Stone body, cold heart, ice body.
I've tried to lose that body on beds and barstools. I've tried to find that body on the same.

When the silver frame on the wall is suspect, the quilt suspect.

When the room that I sleep in becomes unfamiliar.

When my lips shake.

When the body needs holding through a head-to-toe shudder.

Once and then twice.

When the deep belly cry feels so big if I shut my eyes to it, open my mouth to it, fear it will turn me inside out, all 70% water sucked dry to brittle bones.

(Waiting for the trigger to subside.)

I say *I'm scared*. You ask me to tell you why, hold me while I look into the face of it.

Riding out the shockwave, the riptide of nerves fried, how deep the hands of other people touch into me even and most especially when I am being held by new hands that intuitively know how to soothe.

I am so tired of a body that knows multiple lives— each one trying to live through that inescapable splintering of trauma.

It feels too big for me—my body— the rip and tear of who I am in these moments,

how old lives live in me, still.

Fingers typing words of the shapes violence carves in skin.

Holding on for the exorcism.

A ritual:

I want to take care of you.

Bonesy, come lay on top of me.

Place your whole body on my whole body, let's let everything touch and connect.

Rest.

Rest.

Rest.

I want you to let it all go.

Put one thing down that you carry, can you?
Sink in to me.
I can feel you/ can you feel me?
Put all the things down that you carry,
softly,
give them to me, if you can.

Are you able to put something down?
You don't need to carry it all, you can share it with me, release it to
me, settle around me. Sink.
Rest.
Softly rest.

Deep breaths, I love when I can feel them, feel so good when I can
feel them.
Out. In. Out. In. Out. In.

Can you feel that? It's so strong around us.
It feels like an important moment, I'm trying to connect.
Trying to really move into it because it is thick between us,
we are strong, between us.
Don't want to miss the chance
to let go.

Were you able to put something down?
Was it easy to do?
How did it feel?

Pain will make you pure again.[3]

+++

When a fragment of healing comes through collaborative

ethnography, in the form of a poem in response to a piece of embroidery:

Watchers at the Edge[4]

Maybe what we title this could be something really subtle like blood let.

I don't know which my stitches are but I'm keeping track of the fact that you've done most of it.

What is most of it?

One of us bled and one of us did not.
One of us cut, deeply sometimes, and one of us did not.
Sweaty hands produce scars.
Scars are the last to sweat,
sitting on a pair of scissors so you'll find my butt.
Embroidery makes a sound
louder than a scratch that bleeds
which is silence
to my ears.
Pleasing you just by being,
while you embroider.
Pleasing me just by putting the embroidery between us
and still feeling close,
deserving without sweating,
one sweat.

The attention you pay your needle turns me on.

I am tired of absorbing. Carrying. I want to know when to let go, you said. I wonder where your home is? Where in your body are

4   The title— Watchers at the Edge— is borrowed from Sean Donahue's writing about the plant Ghost Pipe

you doing all of this holding? Sometimes you can't tell us apart, the things you do and the things I do.

Hold my feet to the fire and witness the moment when I don't die but actually get reborn.[5]

---

5   This last short piece written in collaboration with Aleksei Wagner.

60

flame to ash

Kat Heatherington

when i think about it for even a moment
i can still feel your pen on my skin,
a too-quick brush of strong fingers
at the nape of my neck,
smoothing the canvas, then holding it, me, down.
cold ink, your warm touch again that i wish would linger,
again the ink, cool and firm and flowing,
attached to the Mystery.
your mind in this moment, this place,
the work of mystery that moves us both.
when you finish you run
the flat of your hand down my spine.
i suppress a shiver.
your dark eyes are open,
warm, and remote.

A Poem for the Closing of Workshops

Zaedryn Meade

We have traveled. Alone and with each other, down deep and up high, from black and white to Technicolor: we are Dorothy in sparkling red shoes who have had the answer all along.

We started as the Ouroboros and we have travelled, have become the scales and spine and beating heart who discovers and devours our own tail, root to crown, recycling, ad infinitum. We complete the circle. We know how we come together to cauldron our stones and thick scented herbs and blue sea glass and red aching scars. We pour our every fluid into the center of the toroid. We are the body, our own body and the body of the circle.

We have become the Alchemist and we have travelled. We have put together our rucksack of tools and took part of the magic, drank of the passionate potion of our pheromonal feast. We made bone from feather, we made heart from stone. We found the scars and massaged until they slip-slided into skin. We bottled the essence of body plus courage plus desire plus prayer.

And now we are closing the circle. Stitching ourselves back up, stepping out into the life flow from this place of stillness and refuge.

When we leave here: again, we will travel, but this time back to whatever we left. Take a breath now into this feeling of the center of the body. Hold it. Lock it to the back of the heart. In the center of the merry-go-round, the tornado, the wheel, the toroid, and the self is the place of stability. On the rim, we are flung. But we have found stillness and we can return.

When we leave here: touch water. Go sit on the edge of the ocean and remember the jagged mountains and green-black kelp and monstrous sharks still under the flat surface. Go find a cobalt waterfall and enter it hand-first, enter it head-first, remember what it feels like to be a body that something rushes against and into. Go find a river that spends half the year as ice and ask how it freezes and thaws and freezes and thaws over and over.

When we leave here: know that with expansion comes contraction. It is the story of the universe, the oldest story, the one even before the sacred whores and healers, the one before the magic rush of one palm on the ground and one palm to the sky. It is a story even the water knows. What we take in may cut to the quick. Be cautious around toxicity, screens, urgency. Expect the contraction, and tend to the baby-green shoots that have dared put their root down and just begun to stretch the surface open.

When we leave here: reach out. We journeyed together and we can look again at each other with blinking eyes and say yes, that happened. Yes, our siren screams of pleasure brought the nourishing rains to soak the soil. Yes, fingers ankles collarbone hips. Yes, hello again beloved.

When we leave here: tell your story. Tell *your* story. Tell the story where we are the hero of our own journey, where our quest is one of continually knowing the self, now and now and now. Leave alone the stories of others, gorgeous and shimmering as they are, lodged as crystals in our open places. They are for our memories, our witness, and we leave them in the circle. Tell your story. Tell it slant. Tell it complete. But always keep a little for yourself.

It is time now to invoke our individuation, to come back into our own completeness. To carry what we have made together, a love note tucked between heart and ribcage. Together, we have traveled. And now together, we are going home.

About the Contributors

Misha Bonaventura's life's purpose is to bring forth a space for passionate creativity through connected inspiration and high integrity. As the founder and vision holder of Trustable Sluts (www. trustablesluts.com) she is dedicated to supporting women in their sexual freedom and social consciousness. She is a communications coach and mediator, events producer and counselor supporting women to be fully sexually expressed. She offers business consulting to sex-positive business owners. She's the creator of Adorata: An Adoration Party for Women (www.adorationforwomen.com), past co-creator of *What is Erotic?* (www.whatiserotic.com) and is a passionate advocate for consent culture, creating safer spaces for women to be their full sexual selves.

Amy Butcher is a co-founder and Chief of Whimsy at Body Trust, a sacred somatic collaborative. She is also a writer, visual artist, and liminal guide. You can learn more about her at amybutcher.com.

Jen Cross is a writer, workshop facilitator, and performer based in the San Francisco Bay area. Most of her writing tangles with queerness, sex, and the aftermath of sexual trauma. She is the author of *Writing Ourselves Whole: Using the Power of Your Own Creativity to Recover and Heal from Sexual Trauma* (Mango, 2017) and the co-editor of the award-winning *Sex Still Spoken Here: An Erotic Reading Circle Anthology* (with Dr. Carol queen and Amy Butcher); her fiction and creative nonfiction have appeared in more than 50 publications, including *Nobody Passes, Sinister Wisdom, The Healing Art of Writing 2010, 14 Hills*, and *Best Sex Writing 2008*. She has facilitated writing workshops for sexual trauma survivors and others since 2002, and recently completed her MFA in Creative Writing at San Francisco State University. Connect with Jen at: writingourselveswhole.org.

Kat Heatherington is a queer polyamorous poet, sometime artist, pagan, and organic gardener, who lives in Sunflower River intentional community, south of Albuquerque. Her work addresses the interstices of human relationships and the natural world. She has one published book, *The Bones of This Land*, from Swimming With Elephants Publications, 2017, available on amazon.com. Her work can be read at sometimesaparticle.org.

Alex Jade has been professionally exploring the sensate, energetic, erotic, and intelligence of our bodies for the past thirty years. Combining a graduate degree in social work, training in massage and movement therapy, with an intrepid passion for eros, Alex was on the faculty of the Body Electric School for the 17 years, and presented a poster at the ASSECT conference about an innovative program of all genders erotic exploration called *Outside the Boxes*. Alex is currently part of the Body Trust collaboration. Alex's work has been written about in the books *Clitoral Truth* by Rebecca Chalker and *Reclaiming Eros: Sacred Whores and Healers* by Suzanne Blackburn and Margaret Wade.

Megan Jennifer writes memoir and erotica about sex, grief, love, identity, family, therapy, and tangled relationships. She writes about edges, and about experiences and identities that hover at the perimeter. Her work has been published at LiteraryKitchen.com, and she is working on her first book — a kinky, epistolary, erotic memoir.

Elsha LaRossa (elshalarossa.com) is an NYC-based singer, performance artist, and inveterate hedonist. Inspired by the contemporary neo-burlesque movement and influenced by modern pop culture, classic Hollywood films, and the glam rockers of the 1970's, she builds performance pieces based on works by traditional composers, breaking through the old-fashioned formality of classical music with cheeky humor, parody, and the (occasionally literal) stripping away of costumes and masks. A polyamorous BDSM practitioner, Elsha is active in the kink community and enjoys using her art and her writing to illuminate and educate those seeking insight into alternative lifestyles. She can most often be found in the company of reprobates and bohemians, offering her service and hostessing skills to a variety of kink and fetish gatherings in Brooklyn and Manhattan, or collaborating to host multi-media, immersive performances and salons with partner Ms Dorothy Darker.

Karla Linden is a writer, massage therapist and clinical hypnotherapist who finds her home in New Mexico.

Jennifer Patterson is a grief worker who uses plants, breath, words to explore survivorhood, body(ies) and healing. A queer and trans affirming, trauma-informed herbalist and breathwork facilitator, Jennifer offers sliding scale care as a practitioner through her own practice Corpus Ritual and is a member of *The Breathe Network* and *Breathwork for Recovery*. She facilitates writing and breathwork workshops at healing centers, LGBTQ centers, a Hasidic and Orthodox Jewish healing center, a needle exchange and harm reduction clinic, veterans hospitals, online with the *Transformative Language Arts Network*, sexual violence resource centers, at colleges and universities, and in the past, the collective *What Would an HIV Doula Do?*. She is the editor of *Queering Sexual Violence: Radical Voices from Within the Anti- Violence Movement* (2016), lectures across the country, and has had writing published in places like *OCHO: A Journal of Queer Arts, Nat. Brut, The Establishment, HandJob,* and *The Feminist Wire* with new publications forthcoming. She is also the creative nonfiction editor of *Hematopoiesis Press*. A graduate of Goddard College's MA program, Jennifer is finishing a book project focused on translating embodied traumatic experience through somatic practices and critical and creative nonfiction. You can find more at ofthebody.net.

Val Prozorova is a transgender writer living in New Zealand, who makes a habit of challenging gender stereotypes and bringing queer lives to the forefront of his writing. Outside of publishing stories, Vel knits 18 hours a day, forgets to eat, and plans his next adventure overseas, supervised by his cat Flynn and dog Aya. You can find more information about Vel, his stories, and his animals, on his website (www.valprozorovawriter.space), Twitter (@inscripturience), Facebook (/valprozorovawriter) and Instagram (@knitfixandchai).

Cooper Taite lives in Minnesota where he works as an educator and writer. When he is not traveling or on the phone in meetings, he enjoys learning and reading anything he can get his hands on. He has worked in the past on the theories of Merleau-Ponty as applied to film theory and comics. He has now begun to explore and apply those theories to the body's many erotic functions. When he has a free weekend, he likes to spend an inordinate amount of time in the kitchen.

Porter Witsell lives and moves between a tiny border town in the Arizona desert and Buenos Aires, Argentina. She is preoccupied with putting water in the desert, working EMS at a very small fire station, and dancing on the community center kid stage after hours. Contact her at eleanormariewitsell@gmail.com.

About the Editor

Zaedryn Meade (they/them) is a writer and speaker whose work is focused on genders, sexualities, and relationships through individual, interpersonal, and institutional power.

Their writing has been widely published online, in dozens of erotica anthologies, and in non-fiction anthologies such as *The Remedy: Trans and Queer Writers on Health and Healthcare; Queering Sexual Violence; Queer: A Reader for Writers*; and *Persistence: All Ways Butch and Femme*. They have edited two erotica anthologies, *Say Please: Lesbian BDSM Erotica* and *Best Lesbian Erotica 2012*, both from Cleis Press.

Sweet & Rough: Queer Kink Erotica, their collection of short stories, was a finalist for the Lambda Literary Lesbian Erotica Award in 2016, and they are the recipient of the NLA-International Cynthia Slater Nonfiction Article award in 2015 and the NLA-International John Preston Short Fiction award in 2016. Zed has been a guest speaker on gender and sexuality at colleges since 2008, and holds degrees in gender studies and creative writing.

About Body Trust

Body Trust, an experiment created by Amy Butcher, Alex Jade, Lizz Randall, and Zaedryn Meade in 2012, is a sacred somatic collaborative dedicated to the body as a laboratory for transformation.

We offer creative projects and workshops to inspire increased capacity for embodiment and connection in order to serve the microcosm of our bodies and the macrocosm of the planet.

We honor the divine wisdom within every body's journey, the power of the erotic realm for healing and integration, and the value of access to all realms of human experience.

We operate within the principles of radical inclusivity, sustainable business, circle technology, and holistic non-binary Tantra. Find out more about our work and join our mailing list for weekly gifts in your inbox at bodytrustcircle.com.

Portals of Pleasure

Advanced annual residential retreat
for women and non-binary folks

Wonder Body

A sophisticated coloring book for curious adults
written by Alex Jade
Illustrated and produced by Amy Butcher

Pleasure Lab

A whimsical podcast
to keep in touch with the world of erotic embodiment

Weekly newsletter & blog posts

Love notes from Amy, Alex, Lizz, and Zed

www.bodytrustcircle.com

Made in the USA
San Bernardino, CA
06 September 2018